This edition published by Parragon Books Ltd in 2014

Parragon Books Ltd
Chartist House
15–17 Trim Street
Bath BA1 1HA, UK
www.parragon.com

ISBN 978-1-4723-6338-1

Printed in Poland

Meet the Pets

Bath • New York • Cologne • Melbourne • Delhi
Hong Kong • Shenzhen • Singapore • Amsterdam

This is a happy tale. It is the tale of four lucky pets who came to be loved by four princesses.

First, there's Pumpkin - a playful pup with soft, fluffy ears. Pumpkin loves to twirl and swirl on her dainty paws. Dance, Pumpkin, dance!

Next, there's Berry - a shy little bunny who lives in the woods. Berry has a twitchy nose and a snowy-white tail. She loves to nibble juicy berries, which is how she got her name, of course!

Then there is Beauty. She's a pretty pink kitty
who likes to curl up in the morning sunshine.

She also naps in the afternoon shade and the evening moonlight. This kitten loves her beauty sleep!

Lastly, there is Blondie – a sweet-natured pony
with a long, golden mane.

Blondie dreams of being a royal horse.

But when she goes to the stables the bigger
horses laugh and say she is too small. Poor Blondie!

All palace pets need a happy home.
When the prince first saw Pumpkin he knew
Cinderella would adore her. He planned to give Pumpkin
to Cinderella as a special anniversary present.

Before long, the palace was Pumpkin's new home
What a lucky pup!

When Snow White first saw Berry, the bunny
was peeking out from behind a blueberry bush.

Berry followed Snow White and her bucket full
of berries and the castle soon became her home.
What a lucky bunny!

Beauty was asleep in the palace garden when the Good Fairies found her. She had rosy fur that shimmered and a tiny nose that glowed.

Aurora had never seen such a beautiful kitten,
and welcomed her into the palace at once.
What a lucky kitty!

When Blondie sneaked in to the royal parade she wanted to show the other horses that she could be like them.

But – oh dear –
she tripped on her mane!

Rapunzel took pity
on the pony and Blondie
became her royal steed,
with her very own stable.
What a lucky pony!

All palace pets love spending time with their princesses.
Pumpkin loves to dance with Cinderella, just as she did
on the night they first met.

She goes to all the palace balls, where she spins and hops all night long.

Pumpkin is so happy she can't stop twirling!

Berry loves to watch Snow White baking.
When Snow White bakes a blueberry pie, she makes
sure there are some berries left for her favourite bunny.

Sometimes, as a special treat, she makes Berry a bowl of sweet mashed carrots.

Berry is so happy she can't stop hopping!

Beauty loves being cuddled by Aurora.

The princess sings while Beauty softly snoozes.

Sometimes, they curl up together for long, cuddly naps, waking just in time for some yummy treats.
Beauty is so happy she can't stop purring!

Blondie loves being groomed by Rapunzel. The princess brushes and plaits Blondie's mane and makes her feel very special.

Blondie is so happy she can't stop smiling!

Like all princesses, Rapunzel knows that her
best friend is her pet.

And, like all palace pets, Blondie knows that
a pet's best friend is always their princess.